TAKE IT EASY, CHARLIE BROWN

by Charles M. Schulz

Selected Cartoons from
You'll Flip, Charlie Brown, Vol. 2

A FAWCETT CREST BOOK

Fawcett Publications, Inc., Greenwich, Conn.

TAKE IT EASY, CHARLIE BROWN

This book, prepared especially for Fawcett Publications, Inc.,
comprises the second half of YOU'LL FLIP, CHARLIE BROWN,
and is reprinted by arrangement with Holt, Rinehart & Winston, Inc.

Printed in the United States of America
February 1973

CLOMP!

ALL RIGHT! CUT IT OUT!

I ALWAYS THOUGHT MAKING SNOWMEN WAS SUPPOSED TO BE FUN..

SCHULZ

GOOD GRIEF! IT SNOWED
LAST NIGHT!

SO HERE I AM COVERED BY A
SOFT BLANKET OF SNOW... I
THINK I'LL LEAP UP AND SCATTER
IT IN ALL DIRECTIONS...

NOW Peanuts Jewelry

Each item is 14 Kt. gold finish, hand-crafted cloisonné in brilliant colors, exquisitely designed by Aviva. Items shown in actual size. Complete satisfaction guaranteed or money refunded.

No. 10 pin $3

No. 11 pin $3

No. 12 pin $3

No. 13A pierced $3
No. 13B non-pierced $3

No. 14 pin $3

No. 15 pin $3

No. 16 pin $3

No. 17A pierced $3
No. 17B non-pierced $3

No. 18 pin $3

No. 19 pin $3

No. 20 pin $3

© United Feature Syndicate, Inc. 1971

No. 21 pin $3

No. 22 tie tack $3

No. 23 tie tack $3

No. 24 key chain $3

No. 25 money clip $4

No. 26 tie tack $3

No. 27 tie bar $3

No. 28 cufflinks $4

No. 29 pin $3

Please specify identity number of each item
ordered and add 25¢ for each item to cover
postage and handling. Personal check or
money order. No cash. Send orders to
HAMILTON HOUSE, Cos Cob, Conn. 06807.